24
23
4 3 9
2 10 6
7 1 5
1 2 3 4 5
6 7 8 9 10
10
9
8
7
6
5
4
3
2
1
2 4 6 8 10 12

Mathematics through discovery and practice

"Mathematics is a discovery of relationships and the expression of the relationship in symbolic (or abstract) form . . . . . .

Practice is necessary to fix a concept, once it is understood. Therefore practice should follow, not precede, discovery".

(Curriculum Bulletin No. 1 of the Schools Council.)

Children make their own discoveries about number, if they have suitable experiences, especially in real life situations. Numbers are not met in isolation from language or experience.

Practice in the four rules of Arithmetic is presented in these four carefully graded books of the Ladybird Basic Arithmetic series :-

Book 1 covers the 100 basic facts of addition

Book 2 covers the 100 basic facts of subtraction

***Book 3** covers the 100 basic facts of multiplication

***Book 4** covers the 90 basic facts of division

Each of these 390 essential number combinations is linked with an attractive illustration which offers the maximum help for happy learning.

**Published February 1968*

See also Books 1 - 4 in the Ladybird "Words for Number" Series

Book 1

THE LADYBIRD
BASIC ARITHMETIC SERIES

Addition made easy

by W. MURRAY
(Author of the Ladybird Key Words Reading Scheme)

Publishers: Wills & Hepworth Ltd., Loughborough
First published 1967 © *Printed in England*

1 2 3 4 5 6 7

Write your answers in your exercise book

1 and 1 make 2

2 and 1 make

3 and 1 make

2 and 2 make

8 9 10 11 12

The pictures will help you with your answers

4 and 1 =

1 and 2 =

1 and 3 =

3 and 3 =

3 + 2 =

1 + 0 =

1 + 4 =

4 + 4 =

$0 + 1 =$

$5 + 1 =$

$2 + 3 =$

$5 + 5 =$

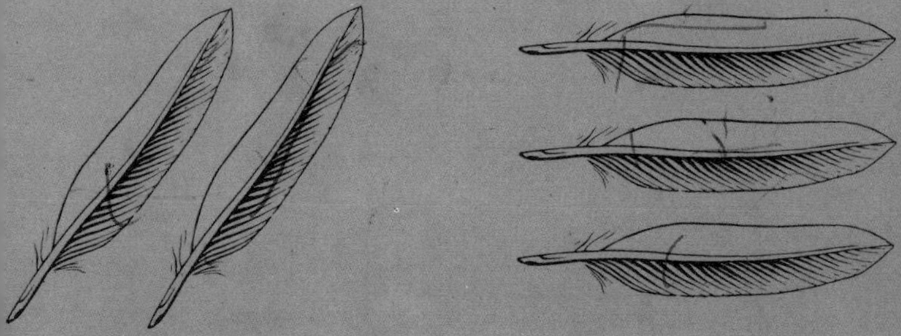
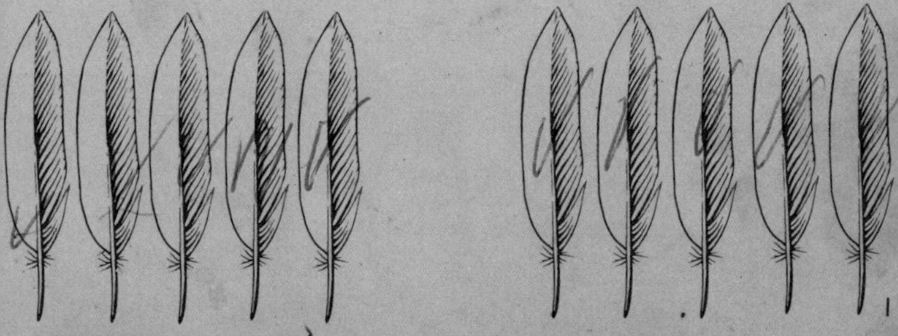

$2 + 0 = 2$

$4 + 2 = 6$

$4 + 3 = 7$

$1 + 5 =$

$4 + 0 =$

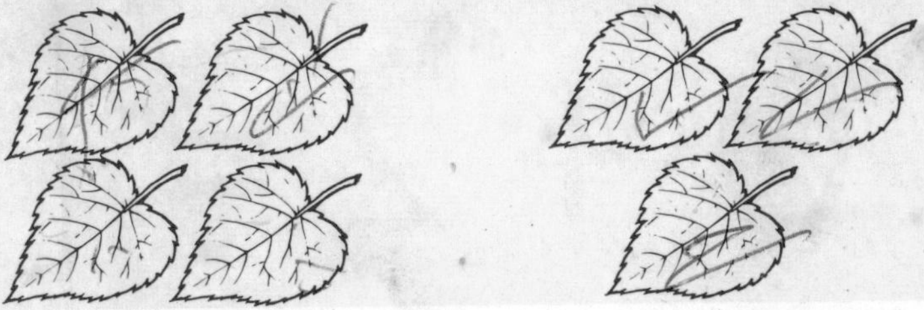

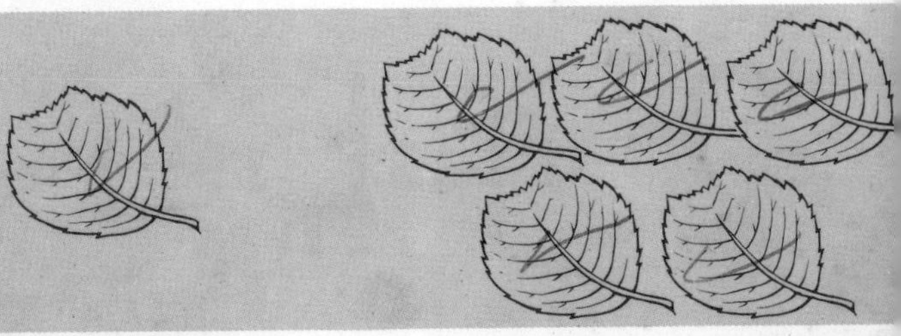

$3 + 4 =$

$6 + 1 =$

$0 + 2 =$

$2 + 4 =$

$0 + 4 =$

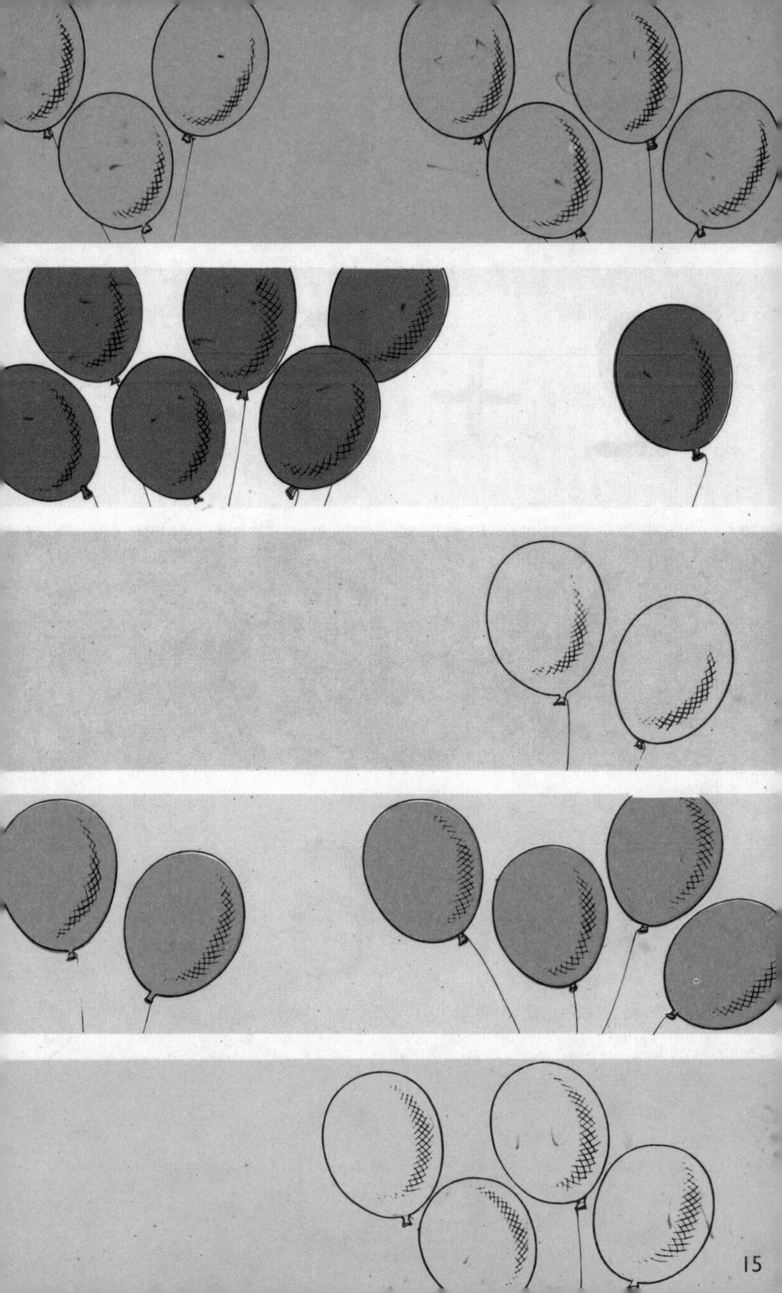

$5 + 4 =$

$2 + 5 =$

$0 + 0 =$

$1 + 6 =$

$3 + 0 =$

$5 + 2 =$

$5 + 0 =$

$4 + 5 =$

$0 + 3 =$

$5 + 3 =$

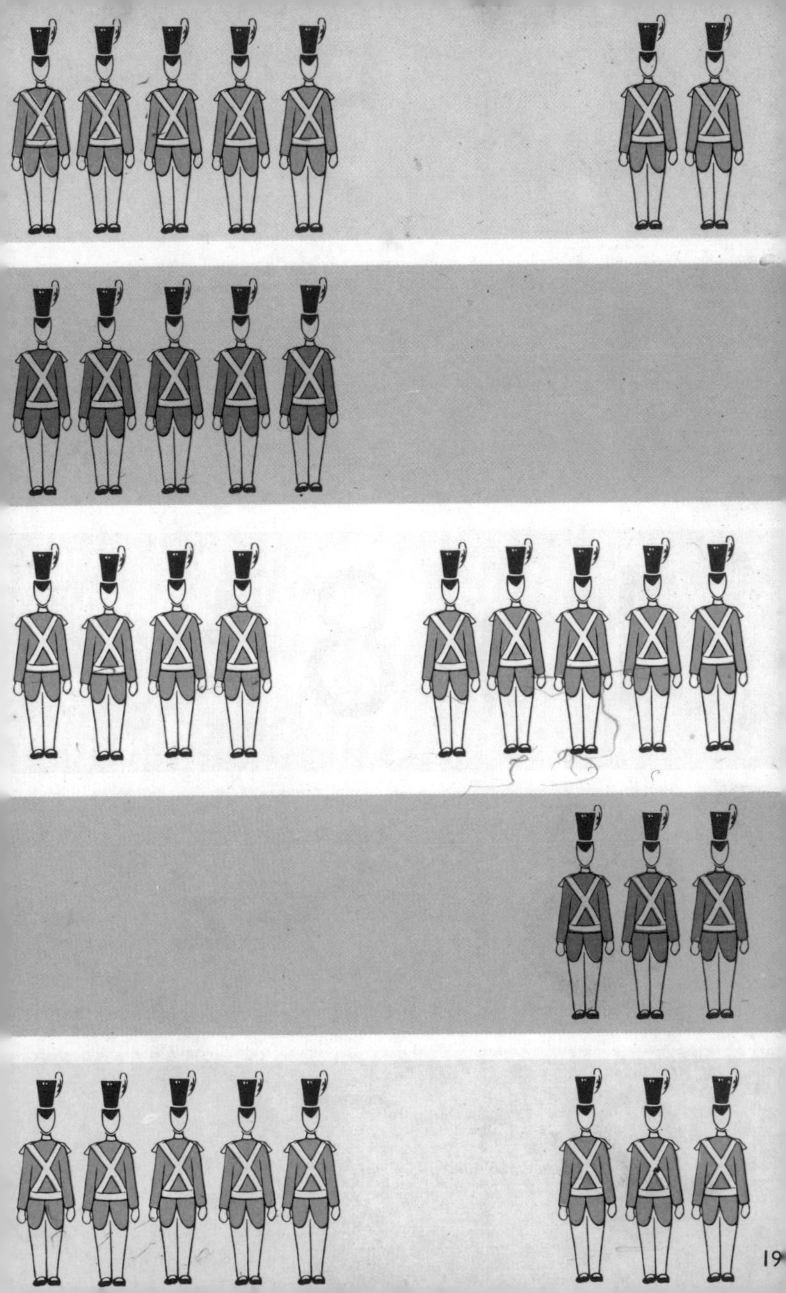

$3 + 5 =$

$7 + 1 =$

$1 + 8 =$

$0 + 5 =$

$0 + 7 =$

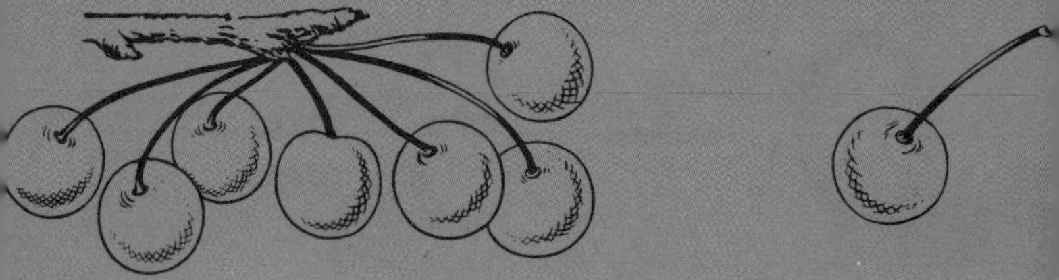

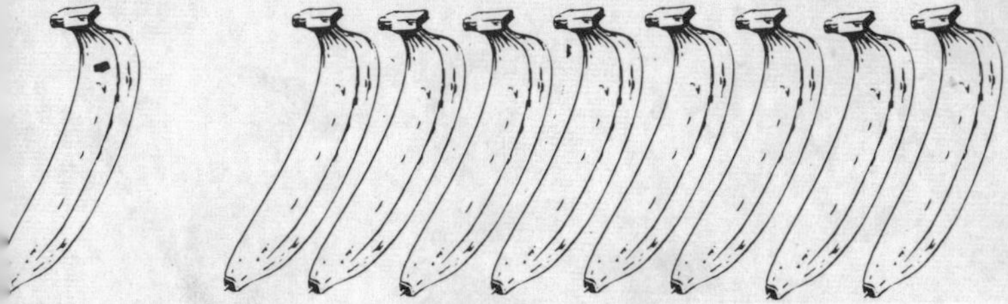

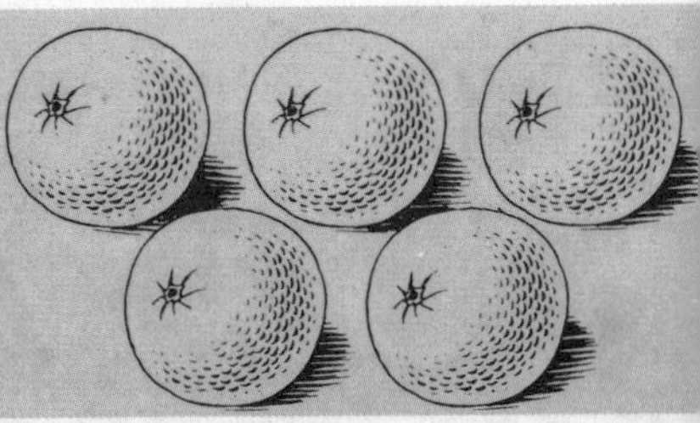

$8 + 1 =$

$0 + 6 =$

$6 + 2 =$

$1 + 7 =$

$7 + 0 =$

$$6 + 0 =$$

$$2 + 6 =$$

$$8 + 0 =$$

$$9 + 1 =$$

$$0 + 9 =$$

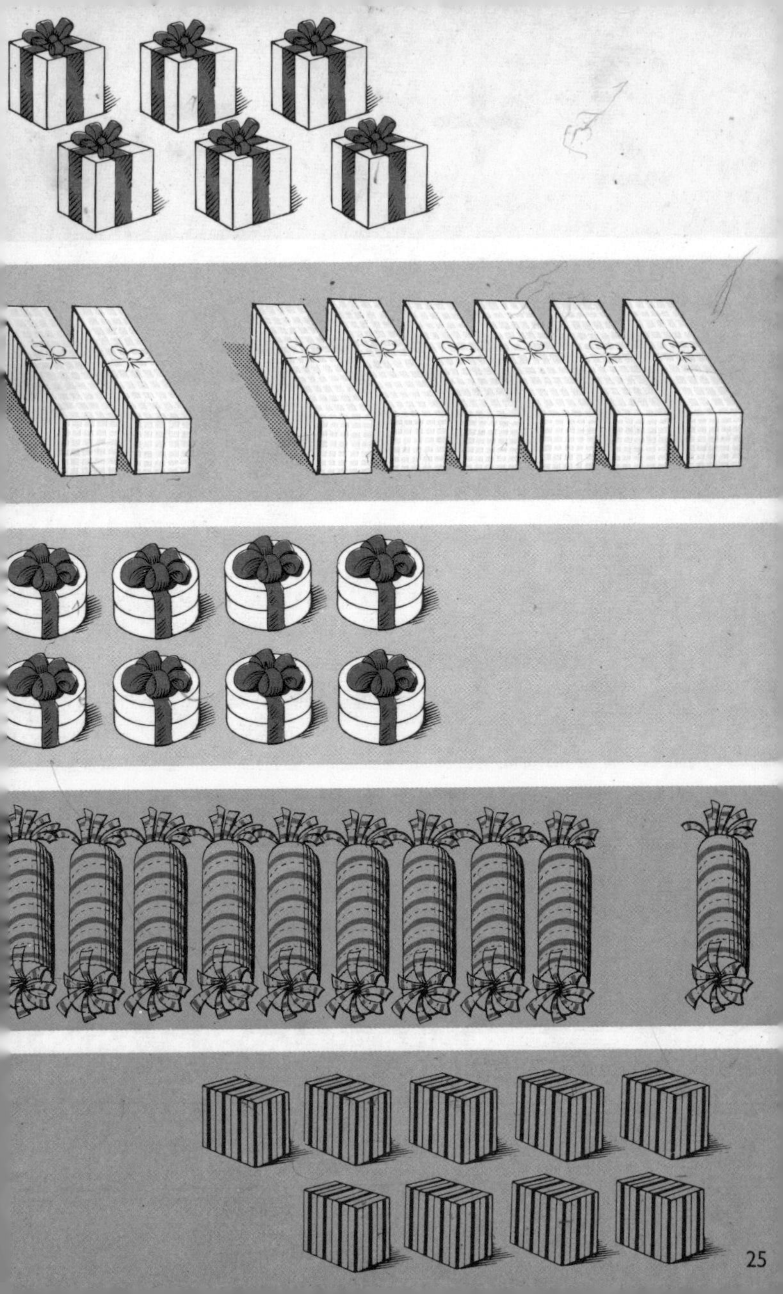

2 + 7 =

1 + 9 =

0 + 8 =

9 + 0 =

2 + 8 =

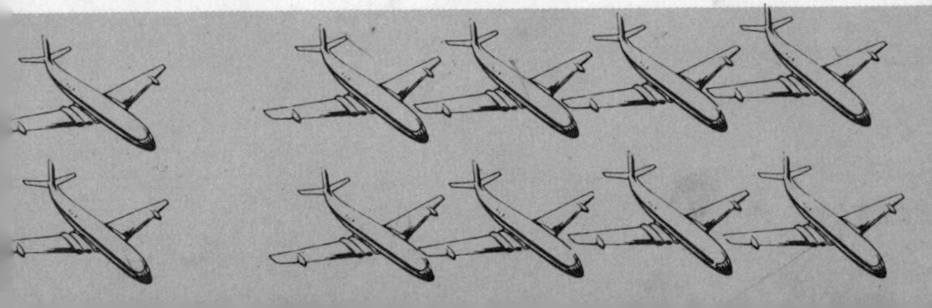

8

+2

10

6

+3

7

+3

7

+2

6

+4

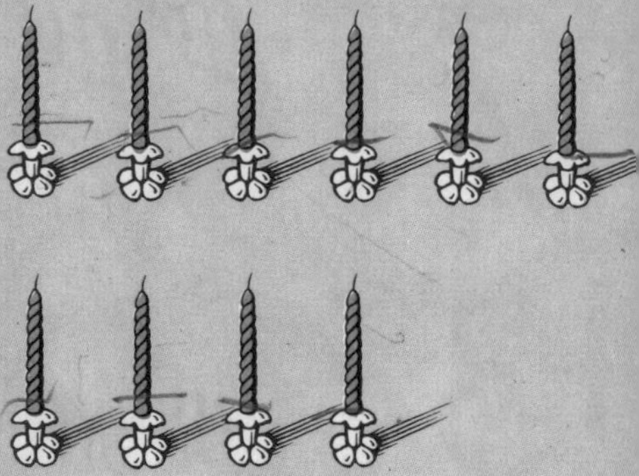

8

+3

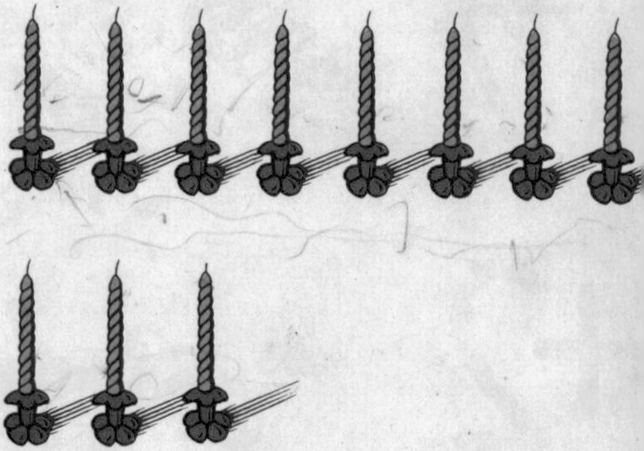

7

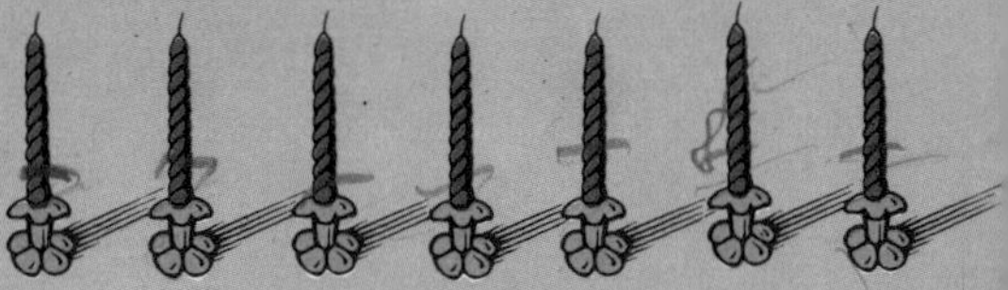

+4

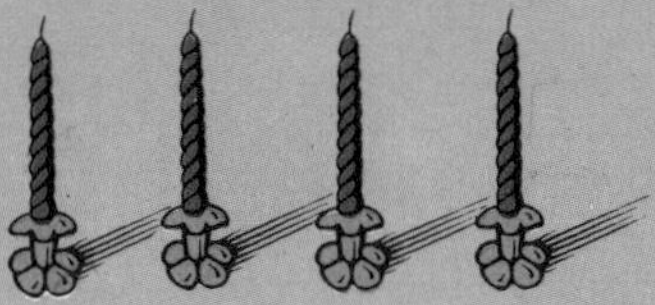

9

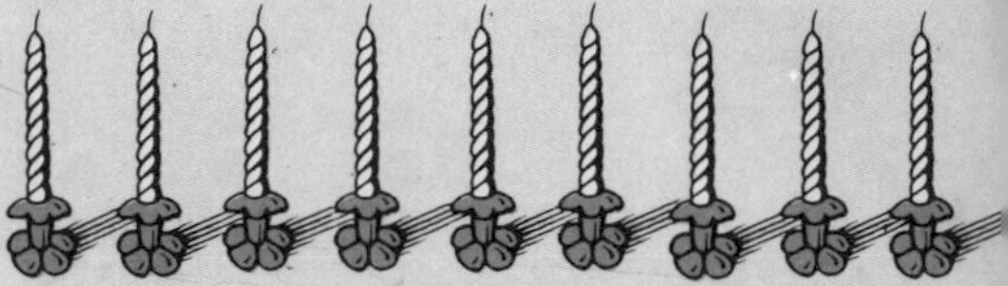

+2

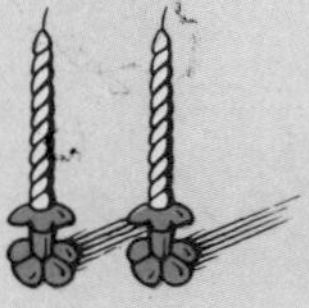

3
+8

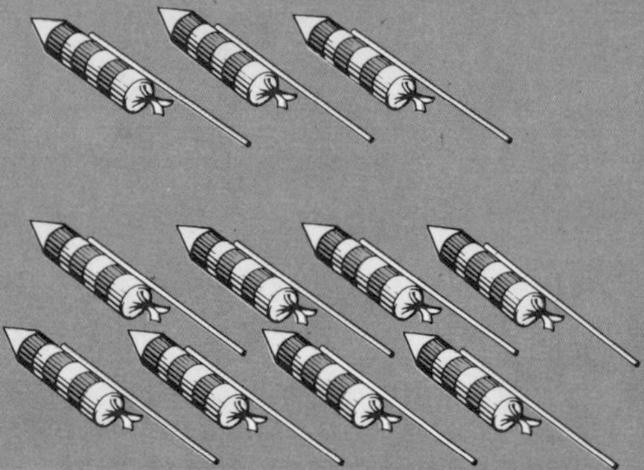

3
+6

3

+7

2

+9

6 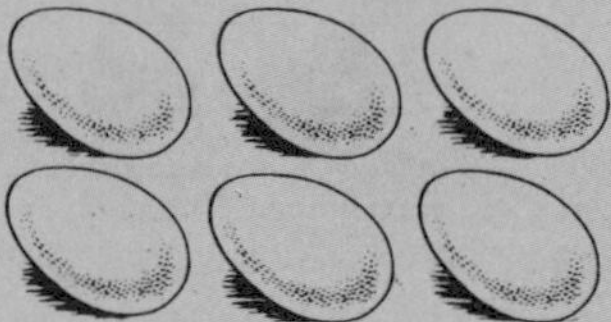

+6 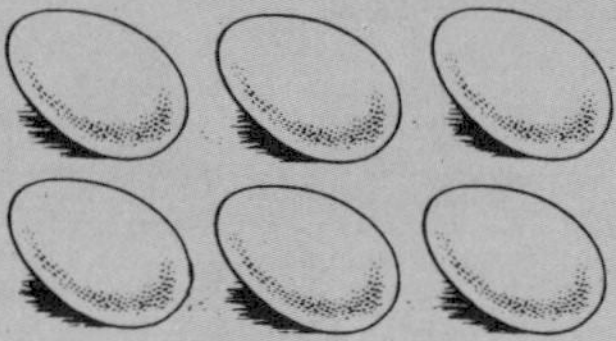

7 

+7 

8

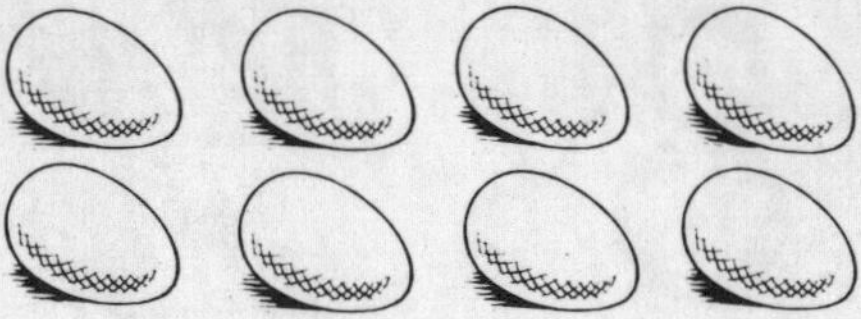

+8

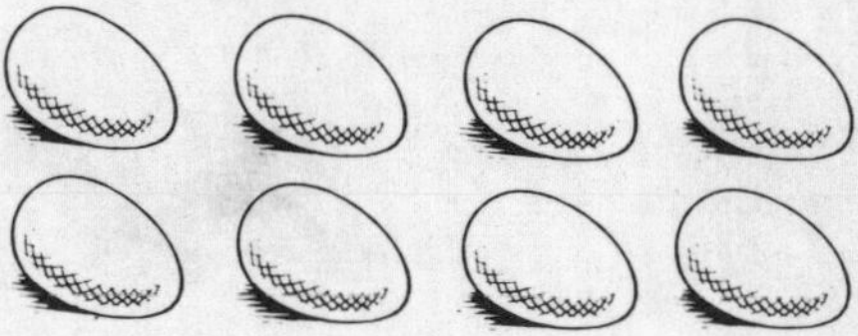

9

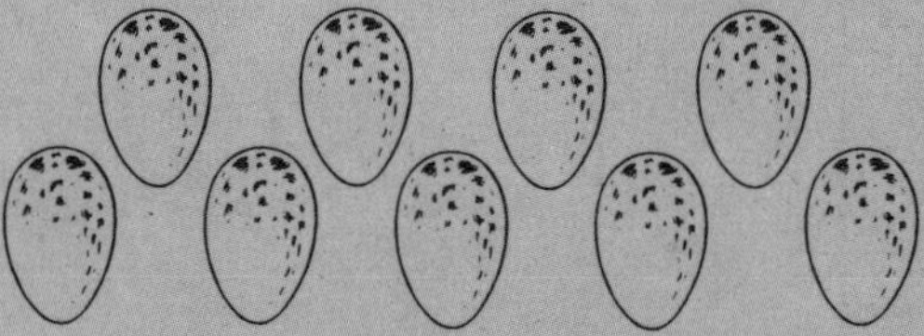

+9

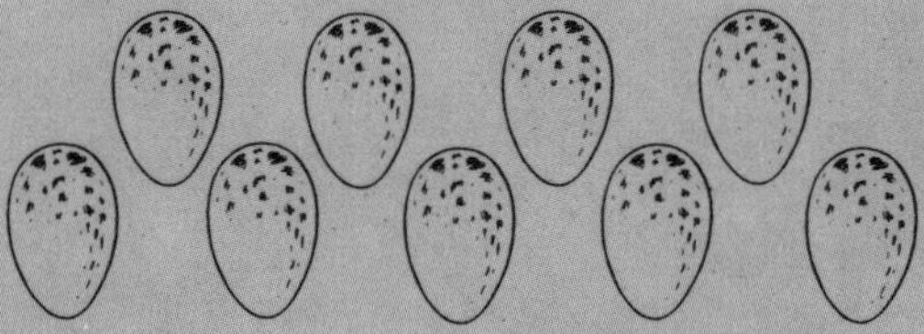

8
+4
___

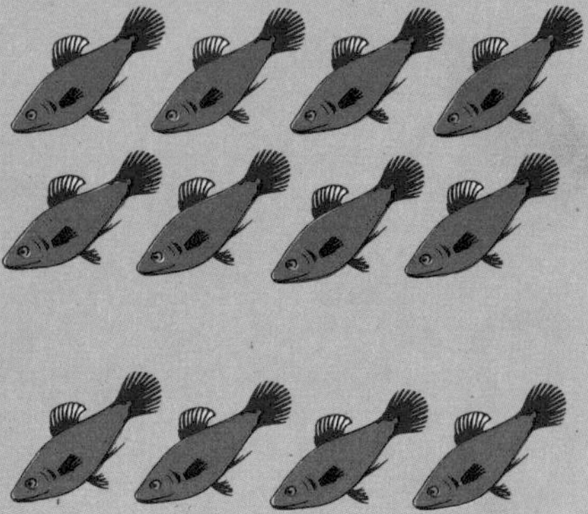

4
+8
___

9

+3

3

+9

  4
+6

___

  6
+5

___

9

+4

7

+5

1

$$\begin{array}{r} 8 \\ +5 \\ \hline \\ \hline \end{array}$$

2

$$\begin{array}{r} 5 \\ +7 \\ \hline \\ \hline \end{array}$$

3

$$\begin{array}{r} 5 \\ +6 \\ \hline \\ \hline \end{array}$$

4

$$\begin{array}{r} 4 \\ +9 \\ \hline \\ \hline \end{array}$$

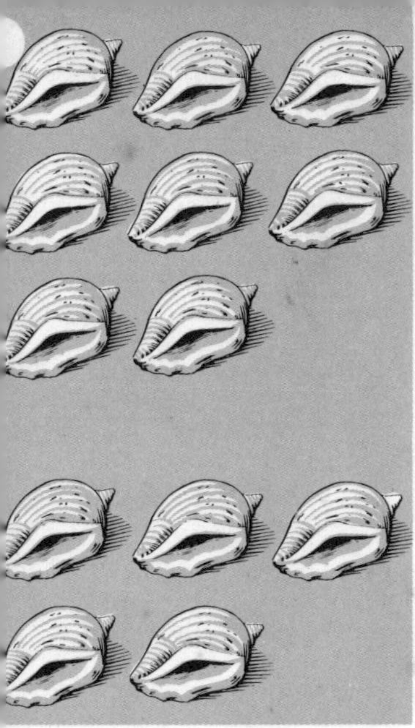

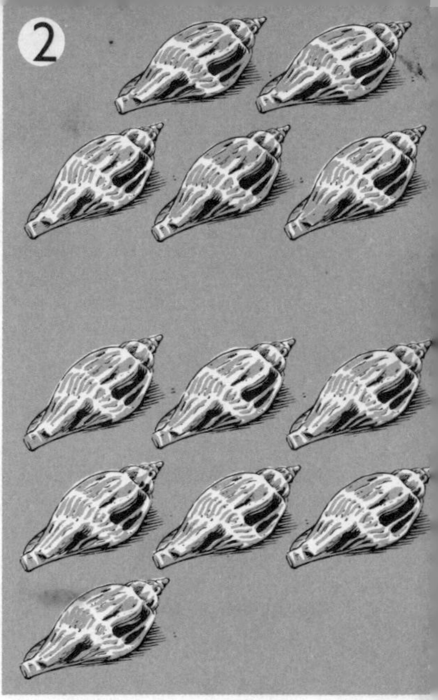
2

4

1

$$\begin{array}{r} 9 \\ +5 \\ \hline \\ \hline \end{array}$$

2

$$\begin{array}{r} 7 \\ +6 \\ \hline \\ \hline \end{array}$$

3

$$\begin{array}{r} 8 \\ +6 \\ \hline \\ \hline \end{array}$$

4

$$\begin{array}{r} 5 \\ +8 \\ \hline \\ \hline \end{array}$$

1

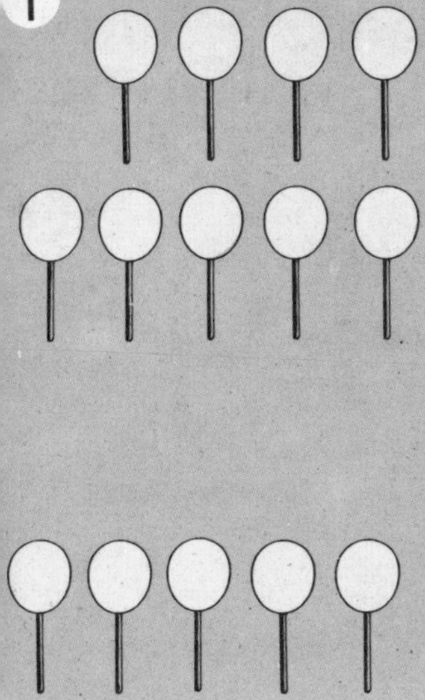

2

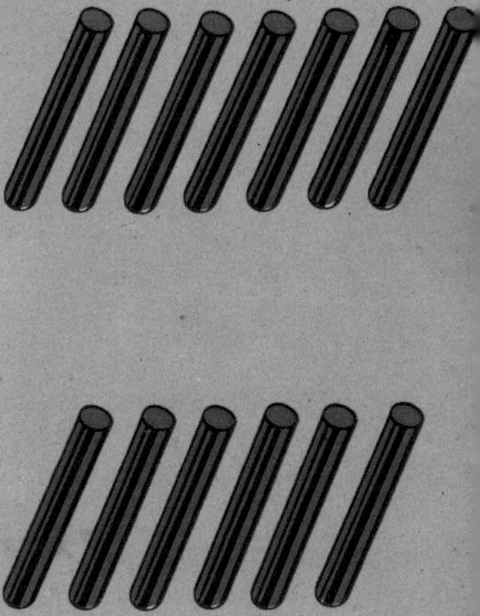

3

4

①

$$\begin{array}{r} 6 \\ +8 \\ \hline \\ \hline \end{array}$$

②

$$\begin{array}{r} 5 \\ +9 \\ \hline \\ \hline \end{array}$$

③

$$\begin{array}{r} 6 \\ +7 \\ \hline \\ \hline \end{array}$$

④

$$\begin{array}{r} 9 \\ +6 \\ \hline \\ \hline \end{array}$$

1

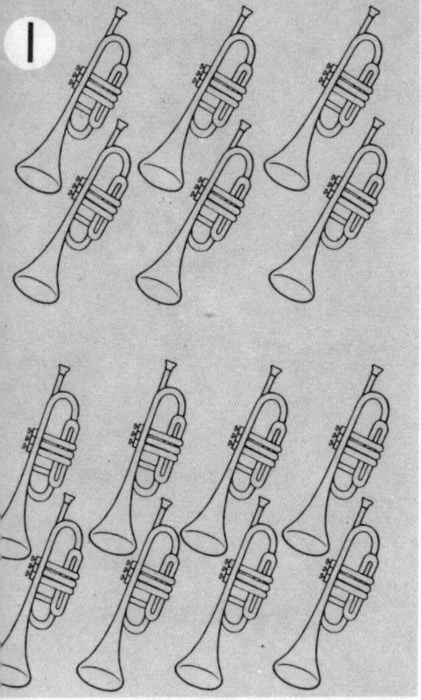

2

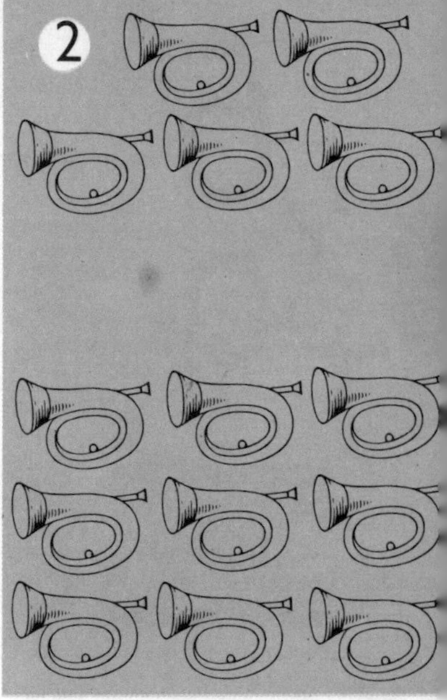

3

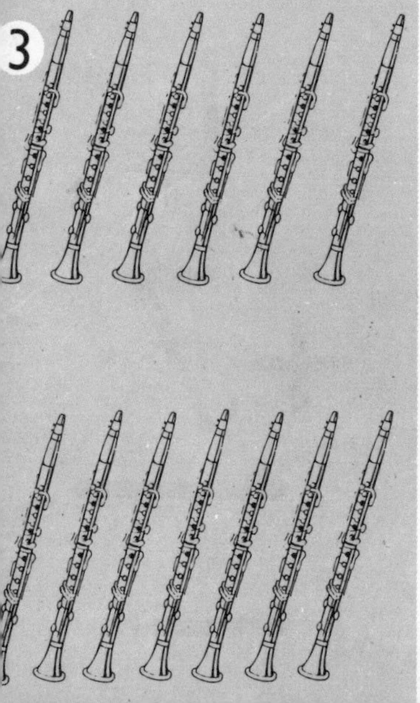

4

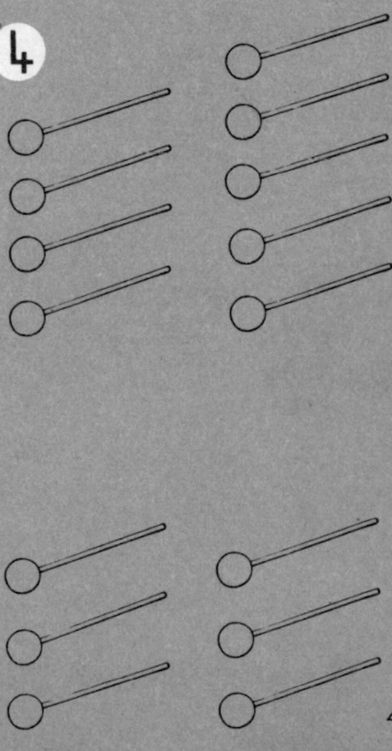

1

$$\begin{array}{r} 6 \\ +9 \\ \hline \\ \hline \end{array}$$

2

$$\begin{array}{r} 8 \\ +7 \\ \hline \\ \hline \end{array}$$

3

$$\begin{array}{r} 9 \\ +7 \\ \hline \\ \hline \end{array}$$

4

$$\begin{array}{r} 4 \\ +7 \\ \hline \\ \hline \end{array}$$

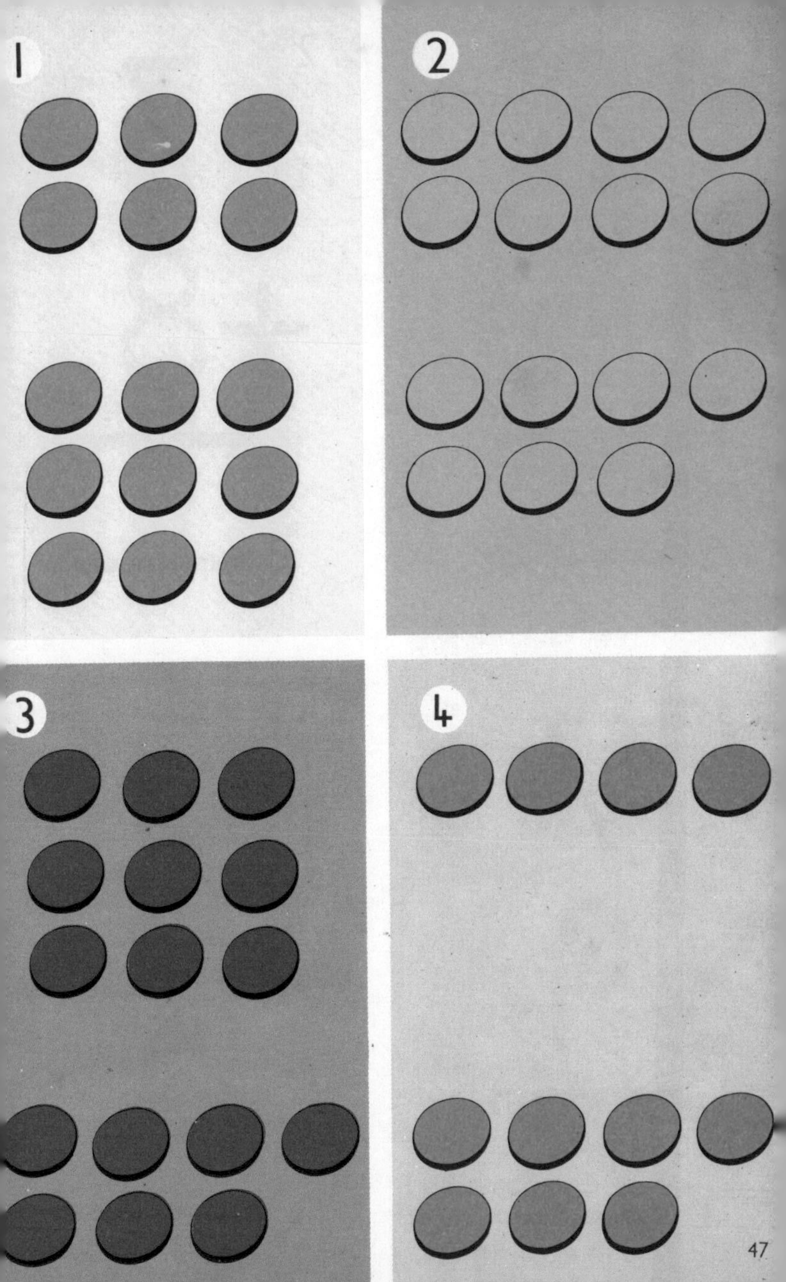
1
2
3
4

1

$$\begin{array}{r} 8 \\ +9 \\ \hline \\ \hline \end{array}$$

2

$$\begin{array}{r} 7 \\ +8 \\ \hline \\ \hline \end{array}$$

3

$$\begin{array}{r} 7 \\ +9 \\ \hline \\ \hline \end{array}$$

4

$$\begin{array}{r} 9 \\ +8 \\ \hline \\ \hline \end{array}$$

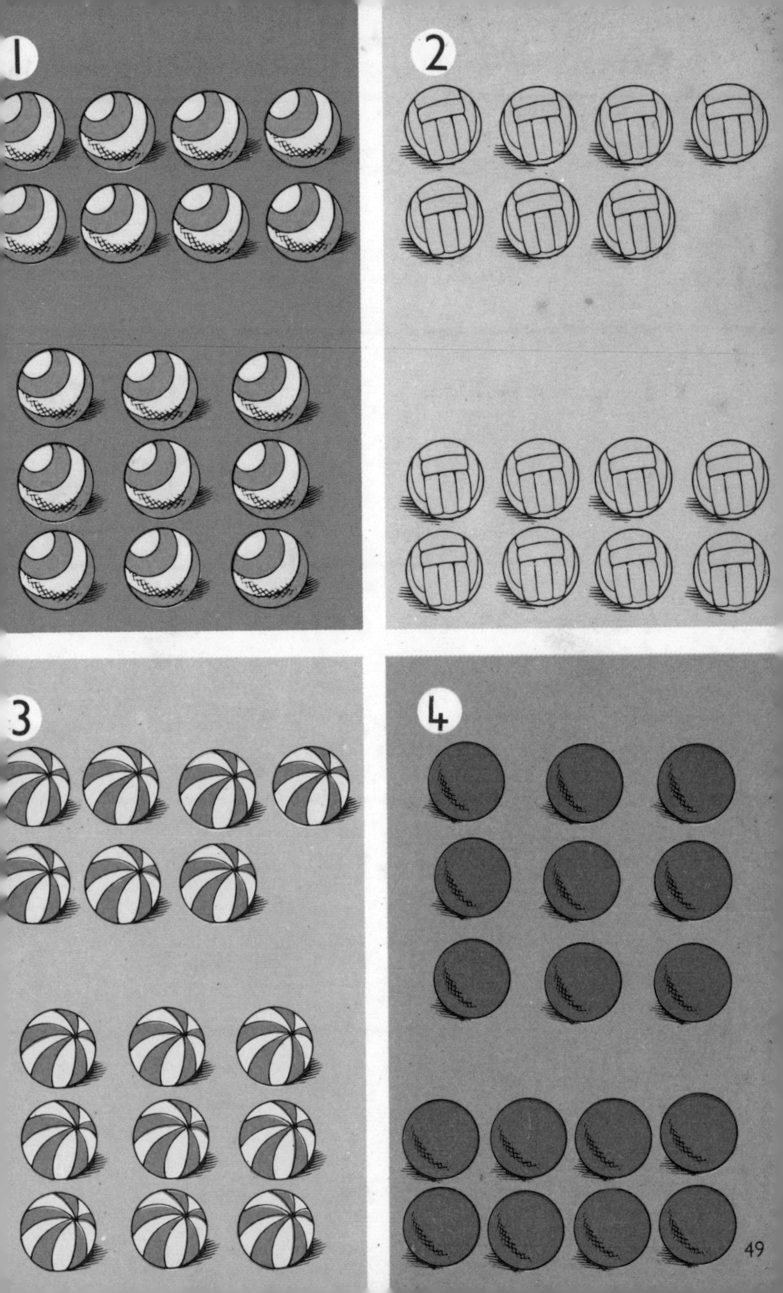
1
2
3
4

TEN TESTS OF TEN SUMS EACH

presenting the 100 basic facts of addition in

Test 1

1 + 1 =	2 + 1 =	3 + 1 =	2 + 2 =	4 + 1 =
1 + 2 =	1 + 3 =	3 + 3 =	3 + 2 =	1 + 0 =

Test 2

1 + 4 =	4 + 4 =	0 + 1 =	5 + 1 =	2 + 3 =
5 + 5 =	2 + 0 =	4 + 2 =	4 + 3 =	1 + 5 =

Test 3

4 + 0 =	3 + 4 =	6 + 1 =	0 + 2 =	2 + 4 =
0 + 4 =	5 + 4 =	2 + 5 =	0 + 0 =	1 + 6 =

Test 4

3 + 0 =	5 + 2 =	5 + 0 =	4 + 5 =	0 + 3 =
5 + 3 =	3 + 5 =	7 + 1 =	1 + 8 =	0 + 5 =

Test 5

0 + 7 =	8 + 1 =	0 + 6 =	6 + 2 =	1 + 7 =
7 + 0 =	6 + 0 =	2 + 6 =	8 + 0 =	9 + 1 =

the order of appearance in this book.

Test 6

0 + 9 =	2 + 7 =	1 + 9 =	0 + 8 =	9 + 0 =
2 + 8 =	8 + 2	6 + 3	7 + 3	7 + 2

Test 7

6 + 4	8 + 3	7 + 4	9 + 2	3 + 8
3 + 6	3 + 7	2 + 9	6 + 6	7 + 7

Test 8

8 + 8	9 + 9	8 + 4	4 + 8	9 + 3
3 + 9	4 + 6	6 + 5	9 + 4	7 + 5

Test 9

8 + 5	5 + 7	5 + 6	4 + 9	9 + 5
7 + 6	8 + 6	5 + 8	6 + 8	5 + 9

Test 10

6 + 7	9 + 6	6 + 9	8 + 7	9 + 7
4 + 7	8 + 9	7 + 8	7 + 9	9 + 8

12
1
2
3
4
5
6
7
8
9
10
11

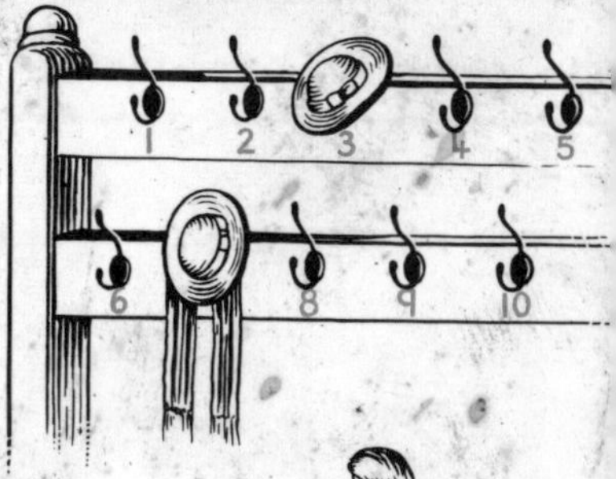

1
2
3
4
5
6
8
9
10

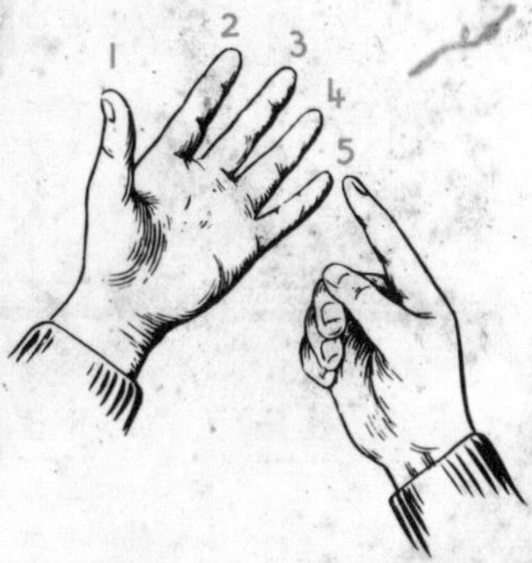

1
2
3
4
5

6
5
4
3
2
1

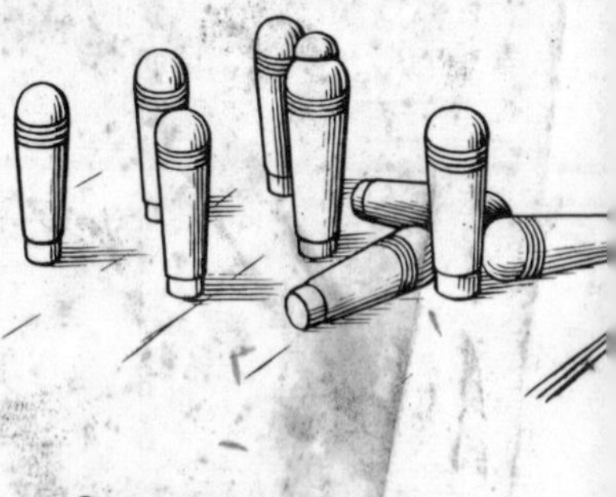

32
25
50
61
71
82
1
13
42
51
47
76
84